An O Away

by Carol Peterson
illustrated by Shirley Beckes

Harcourt
SCHOOL PUBLISHERS

Printed in China

ISBN 10: 0-15-350675-X
ISBN 13: 978-0-15-350675-8

Ordering Options
ISBN 10: 0-15-350600-8 (Grade 3 On-Level Collection)
ISBN 13: 978-0-15-350600-0 (Grade 3 On-Level Collection)
ISBN 10: 0-15-357893-9 (package of 5)
ISBN 13: 978-0-15-357893-9 (package of 5)

4 5 6 7 8 9 10 0940 12 11 10 09

Eric stood at the front desk with the bags as Mom handed the visitor from Florida a key to her room. "There you go, Kate. Enjoy your stay in Zermatt," said Eric's mother.

Eric talked to Kate about Florida whenever he could for the next few days. Before she left, she handed him a slip of paper. "This is my nephew's address," said Kate. "He lives in Tampa, Florida. Why don't you write to him?"

Later Eric sat down at his desk to write a letter to Sam.

Hello Sam,

My name is Eric, and I live in Switzerland. Your Aunt Kate stayed at my family's hotel. She said you would like it if I wrote to you, and I really hope that you do!

I live in a town called Zermatt. It is surrounded by a mountain range called the Alps. The most famous Alp is the Matterhorn. Maybe you have seen pictures of it, but I am including one in case you haven't.

What is it like to live in Florida and be so close to the ocean? I really love alligators. Have you ever seen one? Please write back and tell me about it.

Eric

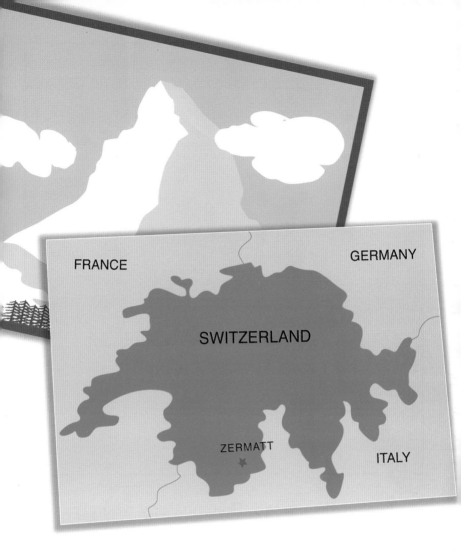

Eric went to the front desk where he found
two postcards. One had a map of Switzerland on
it, and the other had a picture of the Matterhorn.
He sealed the postcards along with his letter in
an envelope and mailed it.

Two weeks passed. Then one day when Eric was helping his father make some repairs to a window, his mother came outside.

She spoke loudly over the din of the pounding hammer. "Eric, here's a letter for you." Eric looked at the envelope and noticed that it was from Florida! He eagerly opened it.

Hello Eric,

Aunt Kate told me about you, and I'm really glad you wrote to me! Florida is sunny and hot. It gets a little cooler in the winter, but not nearly cold enough for snow. I wish we had snow like you. The ocean is blue-green, and the waves are always rolling and heaving.

Once I saw an alligator crossing the street. Cars were dodging it and honking their horns! Here is a picture of one that was in my neighbor's yard.

What language do you speak? Your English is great!

Sam

Eric wrote back right away.

Hello Sam,

The alligator picture is really cool, and everyone at school liked it, too.

Most people here speak German, but we also learn English in school. Our hotel has guests from everywhere. I also speak French, Italian, and Spanish, so sometimes I help translate for them!

The mountains are incredibly beautiful in Switzerland, but I really want to see the ocean. Write soon!

Eric

Eric waited for the mail every day. Finally, Sam's next letter arrived.

Hello Eric,

I speak English and Spanish, so maybe you can teach me some German.

Florida can be fun because we go to the beach. Since my uncle has a boat, we like to fish.

I really want to go to the mountains because I want to ski and snowboard. My family says, "Why do you want to be cold?" Write soon!

Sam

Sam and Uncle Carl

Eric and Sam wrote to each other about what it would be like to travel to far-off places.

"Mom, can't we go to the ocean on our summer vacation?" asked Eric one day.

Mom sighed and replied, "I suppose you mean Florida. Oh, Eric, your sister's just a baby, and it would be so bothersome to travel that far right now. This summer we can go to a lake, and you can swim and sail. All right?"

"All right," said Eric.

It wasn't all right, though, because the lake would not have waves, and it wouldn't go on forever like the ocean either. Eric told Sam about it, and Sam wrote back about a similar problem. His family was planning a winter vacation, and he had suggested skiing in Vermont. They were going to visit relatives in Texas instead.

"I am so disappointed," wrote Sam. "Everyone else said it would be too cold in Vermont. Now I don't think I'll ever get close to a mountain."

Eric thought about it carefully, and then he had an idea. Eric's father took visitors to the Matterhorn every day, so Eric asked to go along the next day. They rode to the base of the mountain. When Eric got out of the van, he searched the ground and located the perfect rock.

That night, Eric placed the rock in a box. He found a piece of paper and wrote, "Here is a rock from the Matterhorn. Now you are close to a mountain!"

Eric mailed it the next day. A few weeks later, he received an envelope from Sam.

Dear Eric,

Thanks for the rock. It's incredible to think that it is actually part of a mountain. It made me feel better, and I hope my gift helps you, too.

Sam

Eric reached into the envelope and slid out a plastic bag. It contained sand and seashells.

Eric poured the sand and shells into a box, and then he placed it on his desk.

Hello Sam,

Thank you for giving me my own little beach. It made me feel better, too. Do you know what? We're both going to get where we want to go some day and that's a promise!

Eric

Think Critically

1. In which parts of the story do you find out about Eric's and Sam's lives?

2. Why doesn't Sam's family want to go to the mountains?

3. How do you think Eric learned so many languages?

4. What causes Eric to find and send a rock to Sam?

5. Do you think Sam and Eric would like it if they traded places?

Social Studies

Different Places, Different Lives Eric and Sam live in two very different places. How are their lives different? How are they the same? Write a paragraph that compares and contrasts their lives and the places that they live.

School-Home Connection Ask family members whether they would prefer to visit the mountains or the beach. Ask them each to explain their choice. Then explain which you would prefer.

Word Count: 906